HÄ

the horrible

chips away

RAVETTE BOOKS

This edition first published by Ravette Books Limited 1991

Printed and Bound
for Ravette Books Limited,
An Egmont Company,
3 Glenside Estate, Star Road, Partridge Green,
Horsham, West Sussex RH13 8RA
by Cox & Wyman Ltd, Reading

ISBN: 1 85304 339 7

HAMLET
LUCKY EDDIE
HÄGAR
HELGA
SNERT
HONI

THERE MUST BE A DIET I CAN STICK TO
THERE IS. YOU EAT ANYTHING YOU WANT AND YOU DON'T HAVE TO EXERCISE

REALLY ? AND YOU LOSE WEIGHT ?
NO
DIK BROWNE
11-1

OH-OH! THEY SAY ANIMALS KNOW WHEN THERE'S TROUBLE IN A HOME

THAT'S AN OLD WIVE'S TALE
DIK BROWNE
11-3

ACCORDING TO THIS MAP, WE HAVE ANOTHER 800 MILES TO GO
THAT'S AWFUL!

MAYBE WE SHOULD'VE GOTTEN A SMALLER MAP
DIK BROWNE
11-4

DID YOU HEAR THE ONE ABOUT...
YES
WELL, THEN—DID YOU HEAR THE ONE ABOUT...
YES
BROWNE
THERE'S NO DOUBT ABOUT IT —I HAVE TO GET SOME NEW MATERIAL
11-5

YOU DON'T DESERVE A WIFE LIKE ME!!
11-7

I'LL DRINK TO THAT!
DIK BROWNE

STAR LIGHT, STAR BRIGHT... FIRST STAR I SEE TONIGHT... I WISH I MAY... I WISH... I'D MEET A REALLY TERRIFIC GUY
11-8

PARDON ME, MISS... BUT I COULDN'T HELP NOTICE...

WE'RE WISHING ON THE SAME STAR
DIK BROWNE

"TOO CRITICAL!" WHERE DOES HE GET OFF TELLING ME I'M TOO CRITICAL?!
11-9
© 1988 King Features Syndicate, Inc. World rights reserved
YOU'RE LATE!
DIK BROWNE

I THINK I'LL STOP ROWING AND ANCHOR A BIT
11-10

DIK BROWNE
WHY HERE ?

I'LL HAVE ANOTHER "DEAD MAN'S RUM" AND NOT SO MUCH SCORPION POISON IN IT THIS TIME!
11-11

WIMP

IT'S NOT THE BETWEEN-MEAL SNACKING THAT'S BLOWING MY DIET
11-12

DIK BROWNE
IT'S THE BETWEEN-SNACK MEALING

SHOULD I BUY A NEW BOAT OR SHOULD I KEEP POURING MONEY INTO REPAIRING MY OLD BOAT?
WHAT KIND OF REPAIRS DOES IT NEED?
IT HAS A LITTLE SCRATCH ON THE BOW
DIK BROWNE
11-14

I'M SORRY—
YOU'RE STUCK
WITH THIS
CONTRACT
HOW CAN THAT BE, COYER?
BEFORE I SIGNED IT
YOU SAID THE FINE PRINT
WAS O.K.
11-15

THEY TRICKED US—
THEY HID IT IN
THE BIG PRINT
DIK
BROWNE

LOOK, ANGELIKA! I GOT A PRINCE! I FOUND HIM AT THE MARKET!
11-16
THAT'S FUNNY. I WAS AT THE MARKET YESTERDAY AND THEY WERE ALL OUT OF HIM
DIK BROWNE

HAGAR! THAT MAN INSULTED ME!
HE CALLED ME "CURVACEOUS"
11-17
BUT THAT ISN'T AN INSULT
IT ISN'T?
SORRY
DIK BROWNE

SIGH "YOU CAN'T GO HOME AGAIN"
11-18

FLOOR STILL WET ?
DIK BROWNE

THE PATIENT IS 75 POUNDS OVERWEIGHT
DIDN'T I PUT YOU ON A VERY STRICT DIET LAST MONTH ?
NOT THAT I RECALL
© 1988 King Features Syndicate, Inc. World rights reserved
11-19
HE'S ALSO LOSING HIS MEMORY
DIK BROWNE

KISS
SEE YOU LATER

SIGH
SOMEDAY MY PRINCE WILL COMMIT
11-22 DIK BROWNE

I NEED SOMEONE TO TAKE OUT THE GARBAGE!
DIK BROWNE

BEAT IT!
11-23

BRING ME A FLAMING DEAD MAN'S RUM !!
ME TOO!
11-24

LOTS OF FRUIT IN MINE !!
DIK BROWNE

WILL THE HOUSE BE OKAY WHILE WE'RE AWAY THIS WEEKEND?
DON'T WORRY. I ASKED LUCKY EDDIE TO HOUSE-SIT FOR US
11-25
DIK BROWNE

THIS IS GOING TO BE TOUGHER THAN I THOUGHT

DID YOU KNOW THE CLOSER YOU GET TO THE NORTH POLE, THE LONGER THE NIGHT IS ?

WE'RE **NOT** MOVING AGAIN!
I'M JUST MAKING CONVERSATION
11-26
DIK BROWNE

HERE COMES DADDY!
YEAHGH!!

I DIDN'T KNOW DADDY COULD SKI!
11·28
DIK BROWNE

THE HUMAN BRAIN IS A WONDERFUL THING. SOMETIMES IN THE WEE SMALL HOURS OF THE MORNING...
WHEN THE BRAIN IS RESTED AND RELAXED I GET MY BEST IDEAS...
DIK BROWNE 11-29

HERE'S TO VICTORY IN TOMORROW'S BATTLE!
HERE'S TO VICTORY IN TOMORROW'S BATTLE!
WHO'S FIGHTING?
11-30
DIK BROWNE

THIS DIET STUFF IS NEVER SWEET ENOUGH!
KISS!
ACTUALLY, IT'S NOT THAT BAD...
WHAT WAS THAT ?
ARTIFICIAL SWEETENER
DIK BROWNE
12-1

HELGA, I STILL CAN'T SLEEP
TRY COUNTING TO 100
12-2
WHAT COMES AFTER 10 ?
BROWNE

HOW DO I LOVE THEE ? LET ME COUNT THE WAYS...
DON'T COUNT!
SPELL IT OUT!
12-3

THEY SAY, "BEHIND EVERY GREAT MAN IS A GREAT WOMAN"

12-6
BEAT IT!!
DIK BROWNE

TAKE IT EASY! WE'RE GETTING THERE!

AND NEVER SAY I DON'T LOVE YOU!
VOOF!
12-7 DIK BROWNE

WHAT'S THIS?!
IT'S A LEFTOVER DISH I PREPARED

IT TASTES LIKE MUSTARD, MAYONNAISE AND CUT-UP DILL PICKLES OVER BREAD CRUMBS SOAKED IN OIL!
THAT'S ALL I HAD LEFT OVER
12-8
DIK BROWNE

HAGAR, I CAN'T SLEEP—I HAVE A PROBLEM THAT I CAN'T SOLVE!
© 1988 King Features Syndicate, Inc. World rights reserved
ARE YOU ASLEEP?
YES
DARN! NOW I HAVE TO SOLVE IT MYSELF!
DIK BROWNE
12-9

STOP COMPLAINING! YOU'RE THE ONE WHO SAID WE SHOULD DO MORE THINGS TOGETHER AS A FAMILY
©1988 King Features Syndicate, Inc. World rights reserved

I DIDN'T MEAN PAINT THE HOUSE!
12·10
DIK BROWNE

ZZZZ
ZZ

SOUNDS LIKE DADDY GOT UP ON THE WRONG SIDE OF BED
@#
12-13
DIK BROWNE

READY ?
READY !
©1988 King Features Syndicate, Inc. World rights reserved

SOMEDAY, THEY'LL PROBABLY HAVE AN EASIER WAY TO GET TO THE TOP
DIK BROWNE
12-14

HAGAR WANTS US TO MAKE OUR OWN CHRISTMAS GIFTS FOR EACH OTHER THIS YEAR
REALLY? WHAT IS HAGAR MAKING?
A MESS
DIK BROWNE 12-15

I TRY TO SAVE MONEY BUT, EVERY TIME I DO, YOU BUY A NEW BOAT!
DON'T WORRY, BABY — SOME DAY OUR SHIP WILL COME IN

WHAT SHIP ?!!
DIK BROWNE 12-16

I HATE TO SEE A LOOSE STRAW HANGING DOWN FROM MY ROOF
WHUMP!
SIGH
DIK BROWNE 12-17

ARE YOU FEELING MORE LIKE YOURSELF TODAY?
THAT DEPENDS...
WHO AM I ?
12-19
DIK BROWNE

YOU SPILLED SOMETHING ON YOUR BEARSKIN
ULP— WHAT SHOULD I DO?

EAT SOMETHING BROWN
DIK BROWNE 12-20

I FINALLY FOUND THE PERFECT CHRISTMAS TREE
GOOD!
© 1988 King Features Syndicate, Inc. World rights reserved
NO!!
DIK BROWNE 12-21

THERE'S THIS BOY I LIKE...
HAVE YOU TOLD HIM?
NOT IN WORDS
WHAT ELSE IS THERE?
12-22
THE TRADITIONAL METHODS - KICKING, PUNCHING, PULLING HIS HAIR... IGNORING HIM...
DIK BROWNE

MOMMA, DO YOU STILL GET THAT STRANGE TINGLING FEELING INSIDE WHEN DADDY WALKS BY?
YES
DIK BROWNE 12-26

IT'S CALLED "HEARTBURN"

HOW WILL THE DAY BE?
MOSTLY BRIGHT AND SUNNY

AND THE NIGHT?
PROBABLY MUCH DARKER
DIK BROWNE 12-27

THEY SAY DOGS AND THEIR OWNERS GET TO LOOK LIKE EACH OTHER
DIK BROWNE 12-28
YUCK!

MY WIFE HAS THE GIFT OF GAB
...WHAT I WANNA KNOW IS...
DIK BROWNE 12-29
WHERE DO I RETURN IT?
© 1988 King Features Syndicate, Inc. World rights reserved

I KNOW IT'S YOUR BIRTHDAY, BUT HOW LONG ARE YOU GOING TO STAY IN BED ?
UNTIL I GET BREAKFAST IN BED
© 1988 King Features Syndicate, Inc. World rights reserved

IT'S 11:30 IN THE MORNING!!!
MAKE IT BRUNCH
DIK BROWNE 12-30

LATELY, I'VE BEEN SO FORGETFUL THAT HELGA MAKES LISTS OF THINGS I HAVE TO DO
HAS IT HELPED ?
NO...
WHY NOT ?
© 1988 King Features Syndicate, Inc. World rights reserved
DIK BROWNE 12-31
I CAN'T READ

YOU MARRIED ME FOR BETTER OR FOR WORSE!

WELL, YOU'RE HALF RIGHT
DIK BROWNE
1-3

DON'T YOU JUST HATE IT WHEN YOUR BACK ITCHES AND YOU CAN'T REACH THE SPOT ?!!

DIK BROWNE 1-4
SHUT UP!

DID YOU FIND OUT WHAT'S WRONG WITH MY BOAT ?
YES, HERE'S THE BILL

DID YOU FIX IT ALREADY ?
NO, FIXING IS EXTRA
DIK BROWNE 1-5

LOOK AT HOW YOUR FATHER TOSSES HIS CLOTHES EVERYWHERE! GIVE ME A HAND WITH THESE
1-6
DIK BROWNE
© 1989 King Features Syndicate, Inc. World rights reserved

OH! SORRY, DARLING, I DIDN'T SEE YOU THERE!

IT LOOKS LIKE HAGAR FORGOT HELGA'S BIRTHDAY AGAIN
BRINGING HER FLOWERS AND CANDY WON'T HELP

BUT SHE MIGHT GO FOR THE DOVE OF PEACE ON HIS HELMET
DIK BROWNE 1-7

DIRTY DIRK, WHERE HAVE YOU BEEN ?

DIK BROWNE
1-9
DIRTY DANCING

MOM, WHERE DOES MILK COME FROM ?
COWS
WHERE DO COWS COME FROM ?
DRINK YOUR MILK
1-10
DIK BROWNE

HMM! THIS IS INTERESTING!
PHILOSOPHY
© 1989 King Features Syndicate, Inc. World rights reserved

DO YOU THINK TOO MUCH EMPHASIS IS PUT ON MATERIAL POSSESSIONS?
1·11 DIK BROWNE

WHAT'S HOLDING YOU BACK?
IT'S MY OLD BOYFRIEND
1-12
DIK BROWNE

HE'S STILL VERY ATTACHED TO ME

BOY, HAS THAT GUY CHANGED! AND FOR THE BETTER!
REALLY? HOW SO?

HE USED TO BE A TERRIBLE BACK-STABBER
1-13
DIK BROWNE

HAGAR LIKES TO PUT HIS WIFE ON A PEDESTAL
© 1989 King Features Syndicate, Inc. World rights reserved

AND THEN SLIP OFF TO A BAR
GET ME DOWN OFF THIS THING!
1-14
DIK BROWNE

I PROMISED MY DOCTOR I WOULDN'T HAVE ANY-MORE MIDNIGHT SNACKS, AND I WON'T
GOOD
TELL ME WHEN IT'S 12:15
DIK BROWNE 1-17

PSST! IT'S ONLY ME! LUCKY EDDIE!
WHO?

LUCKY EDDIE. MAY I PASS?
WHO?
1/18

LUCKY EDDIE! THIS IS GETTING US NOWHERE FAST!
WHO?
ZZZ
ZZZ

4:00 AND ALL IS WELL!

HOW LONG HAVE WE BEEN HERE, HAGAR?
3 MONTHS, WHY?
1-19
DIK BROWNE

I'M GETTING TIRED OF THE 12 TO 8 WATCH

I THOUGHT YOU SAID THIS HOUSE HAS A VIEW OF THE WATER
1-20

DIK BROWNE
IT DOES!

SO... YOU'RE THE "PRINCE" HONI MET...WHAT DO YOU DO?
DIK BROWNE
1-21
I RULE WITH AN EVEN HAND
CARPENTER, HUH ?

SHH! HE'S COMING!
WELCOME HOME

SURPRISE!!
WELCOME HOME
?
1-23
DIK BROWNE

IT TOOK ME A LONG TIME TO LOSE THE WEIGHT AFTER THE BIRTH OF MY FIRST BABY
1-24

HAGAR NEVER DID
BROWNE

YOU KNOW WHAT I FORGOT TO DO LAST NIGHT BEFORE IT STARTED TO SNOW?
WHAT?

BRING IN THE LAUNDRY THAT WAS HANGING ON THE CLOTHESLINE
1-25
DIK BROWNE

MIND IF I WATCH YOU WORK?
YES, ACTUALLY, I DO!
© 1989 King Features Syndicate, Inc. World rights reserved

SORRY!
DON'T YOU HATE IT WHEN PEOPLE LOOK OVER YOUR SHOULDER?
1-27
DIK BROWNE

HOW DID I GET A NAME LIKE 'HAMLET'?
YOU'RE NAMED AFTER YOUR FAMOUS UNCLE, THE PRINCE OF DENMARK
1-28
DIK BROWNE

I THOUGHT IT WAS BECAUSE WHEN HE WAS BORN HE LOOKED LIKE A SMALL HAM
SHHH!

SUBTLE TASTE...GOOD AROMA...A '29 SOAVE DE POPLIQUOSH DE MARE BLUSH ROSÉ...
DIK BROWNE
1-31

...NORTH END OF THE VINEYARD

I'M SICK AND TIRED OF MY CUSTOMERS COMPLAINING ABOUT THE SO-CALLED INFLATED PRICES I CHARGE FOR BOAT REPAIRS!
2-1
DIK BROWNE

NOW, IF YOU'LL EXCUSE ME, I HAVE TO GO TO LUNCH.
BOAT REPAIRS

I CAN'T EAT THIS! IT'S TOO FATTENING! NO! ICK! EYEW!
YOU SHOULD DO WHAT I DO
2-2

WHAT'S THAT?
HAVE THE CAKE FIRST AND THE GUILT AFTER
DIK BROWNE

© 1989 King Features Syndicate, Inc. World rights reserved
2-3
DIK BROWNE

DON'T TELL ME YOU'RE BRINGING WORK HOME THIS WEEKEND AGAIN!

I'D LIKE TO TAKE OUT YOUR DAUGHTER
NOT SO FAST!
LET'S START YOU ON SOMETHING SIMPLER FIRST
TAKE OUT THE GARBAGE
BROWNE
2-4

I KNOW MEN DON'T LIKE PUSHY, POSSESSIVE WOMEN, HAMLET
BUT CAN I TELL YOU ONE TEENSIE LITTLE THING?
SURE
2-7
WHEN YOU GROW UP YOU'RE **MINE**
BROWNE

I GAVE DIRTY DIRK A BAR OF SOAP AS A SUBTLE HINT TO CLEAN UP HIS ACT
HOW'D HE TAKE IT?
© 1989 King Features Syndicate, Inc. World rights reserved

HE ATE IT
DIK BROWNE 2-8

SVENSON WOULD LIKE TO HAVE A FEW WORDS WITH YOU, SIR

DON'T TELL ME HE WANTS TO TAKE ANOTHER SICK DAY!
2-9
DIK BROWNE

YOU'VE GOT STRESS
GET OUT MORE! TRAVEL! MEET NEW PEOPLE!
2/10
DIK BROWNE
THAT'S HOW I GOT STRESS!

HELGA, DO YOU THINK I COULD...
NO!

BUT YOU DIDN'T EVEN HEAR THE QUESTION YET!
I'M SORRY...
2/11
DIK BROWNE

THAT'S FROM BEING AROUND THE KIDS ALL DAY

I SAY IT'S ONLY A TRICK TO MAKE US TURN BACK...
2/13
DIK BROWNE

BUT JUST TO BE SAFE, LUCKY EDDIE, WHY DON'T YOU GO FIRST ?
DANGER! QUICKSAND AHEAD

CATCH!
2/14
© 1989 King Features Syndicate, Inc. World rights reserved
CRUNCH
GLUG
GLUG
GLUG GLUG
DO YOU KNOW HOW MANY CALORIES ARE IN ONE OF THOSE?

KVACK IS ALL READY
YOU MEAN SHE'S ON A PLATTER SURROUNDED BY POTATOES AND SPRIGS OF PARSLEY ?!

AW, I WAS ONLY JOKING!
2-15
DIK BROWNE

TELL ME THE TRUTH, HELGA...

YOU'RE TIRED OF ME TAKING ALL THE COVERS AT NIGHT, AREN'T YOU?
2/16
DIK BROWNE

THIS HOUSE HAS A NICE VIEW AND YOU HAVE LOTS OF PRIVACY...

PLUS YOU DON'T HAVE TO WORRY ABOUT WATER IN THE BASEMENT
2/18
DIK BROWNE

I WANT A PRIVATE BATH!
2/21
DIK BROWNE

IT'S A SHAME TO WASTE THE WATER!

IT'S BEEN DIFFICULT TRYING TO PICK SOMEONE TO GUARD OUR CAMP WHILE THE REST OF US GO OFF TO BATTLE
2/22
DIK BROWNE

BUT I THINK I'VE FINALLY REACHED A DECISION

I'LL NEVER FORGET WHAT HAGAR SAID WHEN HE PROPOSED...
"MARRY ME AND I'LL GIVE YOU EVERYTHING YOUR LITTLE HEART CAN ASK FOR"
2/23
DIK BROWNE
HE KNEW HEARTS CAN'T TALK, RIGHT?
RIGHT

WHAT DAY IS TODAY ?
FRIDAY
DIK BROWNE
2/24
© 1989 King Features Syndicate, Inc. World rights reserved
WHY DON'T WE HAVE A "THANK GOD" IT'S FRIDAY" PARTY FOR OLD TIME'S SAKE ?

NOW DON'T EMBARRASS ME BY ORDERING **MILK** IN A TOUGH BAR LIKE THIS!
BUT I **LIKE** MILK!
OKAY, BUT AT LEAST ORDER A SHOT OF SOMETHING WITH IT!
2/25
DIK BROWNE
I'D LIKE A TALL, COOL GLASS OF MILK WITH A SHOT OF CHOCOLATE SYRUP ON THE SIDE

WHAT A DISH!
2/28
DIK BROWNE

OW!!
NOT ON YOUR DIET!

THEY SAY WHEN YOU'RE UPTIGHT THE SECRET IS TO LAUGH AWAY THE TENSION

HEARD ANY FUNNY STORIES LATELY ?
3-1
BROWNE

MAKE THEM AN OFFER— THEY SEEM ANXIOUS TO SELL!
DIK BROWNE 3-2
© 1989 King Features Syndicate, Inc. World rights reserved

FOR SALE

ARE YOU THE GUYS WHO ASKED US TO SEND OUT OUR TOUGHEST MAN?
YES
3/3

HE'LL BE RIGHT HERE. HE'S PARKING HIS GRIZZLY!
HOO BOY!
DIK BROWNE

BROTHER HAGAR, I AM HERE TO TELL YOU IT'S NEVER TOO LATE TO CHANGE

HEY, BARNEY, MAKE THAT A LITE BEER!
DIK BROWNE 3/4

WHY DO YOU HAVE TO DRINK AT EVERY MEAL?
AUTHORITIES SAY IT'S BENEFICIAL TO WASH DOWN BULKY FIBROUS FOODS WITH A GLASS OF WINE...
3/7
YOU'RE HAVING TOMATO SOUP
DIK BROWNE

SIGH I HATE TO GO HOME. MY MOTHER-IN-LAW IS VISITING FOR A MONTH
A MONTH? YOU POOR DEVIL!
DIK BROWNE
3-8
IT'S WORSE THAN YOU THINK
I'M DIVORCED

I'LL ORDER FOR BOTH OF US
VERY GOOD, SIR
ROAST BEEF... FRIED CHICKEN...GLAZED HAM... AND, FOR DESSERT, SMOKED SAUSAGE...
3/9
© 1989 King Features Syndicate, Inc. World rights reserved
IT'S HIS BIRTHDAY
DIK BROWNE

YOU KNOW HOW, WHEN I GET DEPRESSED, I SHOP? AND WHEN I'M *REALLY* DEPRESSED I SHOP EVEN MORE?
YEAH... HA, HA
DIK BROWNE
WELL, TODAY I WAS DOWNRIGHT **DESPONDENT**!
3/10

WILL DADDY BE HOME FOR LUNCH?
NO, HE SAID HE WAS HAVING LUNCH WITH A CLIENT
© 1989 King Features Syndicate, Inc. World rights reserved

DIK BROWNE
3/11

WE BETTER STOP TO REFUEL
GOOD IDEA

BAR
3-13

YOU'VE BEEN DRINKING AT THE BAR AGAIN, HAVEN'T YOU ?
WHAT GAVE YOU THAT IDEA ?
3-14
DIK BROWNE

A WIFE CAN ALWAYS TELL

NOW, WHAT'S THIS STRING SUPPOSED TO REMIND ME OF ?
3-15
DIK BROWNE

OH, YEAH! TAKE OUT THE GARBAGE

HELGA LOVES THE NEW MIRROR I GOT HER
3-16
© 1989 King Features Syndicate, Inc. World rights reserved

I DO THINK I LOOK SLIMMER
DIK BROWNE

I THINK I'LL HAVE MY *USUAL*
WHAT'S YOUR USUAL ?
3-17

IT'S WHAT I ALWAYS HAVE
DIK BROWNE

YOU TOLD ME LAST WEEK YOU'D CHECK MY BOAT AND YOU STILL HAVEN'T DONE IT!
ALL RIGHT! ALL RIGHT! I'LL CHECK YOUR BOAT!!

THEY'RE SO INDEPENDENT!
DIK BROWNE 3-18

TWO FEET, HAGAR... **TWO** FEET!
DIK BROWNE

THIS SCALE IS CROOKED!
3-21

SURE, BEING GROWN UP IS FUN! YOU GET TO GO ON VOYAGES, FIGHT BATTLES, STAY UP LATE!
DIK BROWNE

DO YOU HAVE TO GET MARRIED?
3-22

BOY, IT'S GOOD TO BE HOME!
DIK BROWNE

HOW WAS AFRICA?
3-23

I HATE FANCY PARTIES! I NEVER KNOW HOW TO ACT!
JUST BE YOURSELF AND YOU'LL BE FINE
3-24
DIK BROWNE
ON THE OTHER HAND...
P-TUI!

I DESERVE TO RELAX! I GOT 54 PEOPLE WHO DEPEND ON ME FOR A LIVING!
DIK BROWNE 3-25

55 — YOU FORGOT LOUIE THE BARTENDER!
SLAM!

HOW'S THE CATAPULT COMING, LUCKY EDDIE ?
DIK BROWNE

GOOD!
I FINALLY GOT THE BUGS OUT!
3-27

I KNOW I'M LATE! BUT I EXPECT FOOD ON THE TABLE AS SOON AS I SIT DOWN!
3-28
SPLAT!
DIK BROWNE
ON A PLATE!

WORK! WORK! WORK!
AND WHAT DO I GET FOR IT?
DIK BROWNE

LOOT! LOOT! LOOT!
WHO ASKED YOU ?!
3-29

THE SECRET TO EATING SMORGASBORD IS NOT TO LOAD UP WITH A LOT OF DIFFERENT FOODS...
3-30

JUST TAKE A FEW OF THE THINGS YOU REALLY LIKE !

DON'T LIE TO ME. YOU WENT TO LUCKY EDDIE'S BIRTHDAY PARTY, DIDN'T YOU?
WHAT MAKES YOU SAY THAT?
3-31

CALL IT A LUCKY GUESS

WHAT SHOULD I DO WITH THIS PORTRAIT?
HANG IT
4-1

HANGIN'S TOO GOOD FOR IT
DIK BROWNE

THE INSIDE OF YOUR HOUSE SEEMS LARGER — DID YOU DO SOMETHING TO IT ?
YES

HELGA MADE ME REDESIGN THE BAR
XXX
4-4
DIK BROWNE

CAN YOU FIX MY BOAT TODAY?
MAYBE
4-5
DIK BROWNE
© 1989 King Features Syndicate, Inc. World rights reserved

WHAT'S THE PROBLEM?
REPAIRS

MY WIFE DOESN'T UNDERSTAND ME...
YOUR WIFE DOESN'T UNDERSTAND YOU ?! LISTEN TO ME...

I CAN'T STAND BELLYACHING BARTENDERS

I WANT A BOTTLE OF WINE
WHAT YEAR?
© 1989 King Features Syndicate, Inc. World rights reserved

THINGS COULD GET PRETTY NASTY IF I DON'T GET IT *THIS* YEAR
4-7
DIK BROWNE

IF IT WEREN'T FOR WOMEN, MEN WOULD NEVER WASH OR CHANGE CLOTHES, THEY'D EAT ALL THE WRONG FOODS, AND NEVER PICK UP THEIR CLOTHES
CAN YOU IMAGINE WHAT KIND OF WORLD THAT WOULD BE ?
YEAH!!
4/8
DIK BROWNE

YOU LOST THE ANCHOR?!
I THINK YOU'RE GETTING DUMBER EVERY DAY!
I AM?

THESE MUST BE MY PEAK YEARS!
4-11
DIK BROWNE

LUCKY EDDIE, DID YOU REMOVE THE GANGPLANK?
WHY?

WHEN HAGAR TRIED TO COME ABOARD, HE FELL OVERBOARD AND LOST A BOTTLE OF TWENTY-YEAR-OLD BRANDY
DIK BROWNE

THEN, NO
4-12

I'M AFRAID SOMEDAY I'M GONNA SPREAD MYSELF TOO THIN

FAT CHANCE
4-13 BROWNE